Developing Numeracy

CALCULATIONS

ACTIVITIES FOR THE DAILY MATHS LESSON

ADDING AND SUBTRACTING

year

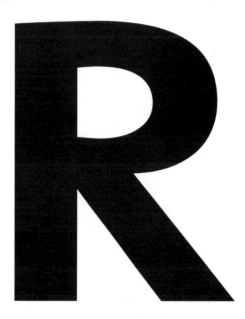

Peter Patilla

A & C BLACK

Contents

Adding and subtracting

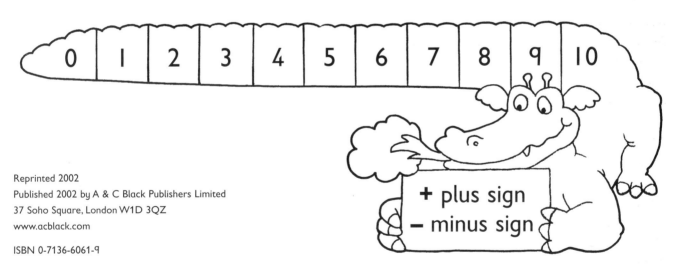

Reprinted 2002

Published 2002 by A & C Black Publishers Limited

37 Soho Square, London W1D 3QZ

www.acblack.com

ISBN 0-7136-6061-9

The author and publishers would like to thank Madeleine Madden and Corinne McCrum for their advice in producing this series of books.

A CIP catalogue record for this book is available from the British Library.

A & C Black uses paper produced with elemental chlorine-free pulp, harvested from managed sustainable forests.

Printed in Great Britain by Caligraving Ltd, Thetford, Norfolk.

Introduction

Developing Numeracy: Calculations is a series of seven photocopiable activity books designed to be used during the daily maths lesson. They focus on the second strand of the National Numeracy Strategy *Framework for teaching mathematics*. The activities are intended to be used in the time allocated to pupil activities; they aim to reinforce the knowledge, understanding and skills taught during the main part of the lesson and to provide practice and consolidation of the objectives contained in the framework document.

Year R supports the teaching of mathematics by providing a series of activities which develop important calculation skills. On the whole the activities are designed for children to work on independently, although due to the young age of the children, the teacher may need to read the instructions with the children and ensure that they understand the activity before they begin working on it.

Year R encourages children to:
- use the vocabulary involved in adding and subtracting;
- find one more or one less than a number from 1 to 10;
- relate addition to combining groups of objects;
- relate addition to counting on;
- double small numbers by counting on;
- separate (partition) groups into two or more sets;
- select two groups to match a given total;
- subtract by taking away;
- subtract by counting back;
- find simple differences by counting on;
- work out how many objects in a group are hidden by counting on.

Extension

Many of the activity sheets end with a challenge (**Now try this!**) which reinforces and extends the children's learning, and provides the teacher with the opportunity for assessment. Again, it may be necessary to read  the instructions with the children before they begin the activity. For some of the challenges the children will need to record their answers on a separate piece of paper.

Organisation

Very little equipment is needed, but it will be useful to have available: coloured pencils, counters, scissors, dice, coins, number lines and number tracks. Other useful counting equipment includes unit apparatus, such as interlocking cubes, and rod apparatus, such as number rods. To help children understand concepts and develop a wide range of mathematical language, they should have regular opportunities to use both unit and rod apparatus.

The activities in this book will naturally bring in elements of counting and problem solving. Children need to be confident and efficient in counting to be able to develop their calculation skills effectively. They will need regular counting practice to consolidate and develop the skills outlined in the Numbers and the Number System strand of the Strategy for Year R (see **Developing Numeracy: Numbers and the Number System Year R**).

To help teachers select appropriate learning experiences for the children, the activities are grouped into sections within this book. However, the activities are not expected to be used in that order; the sheets are intended to support, rather than direct, the teacher's planning.

Some activities are deliberately more challenging than others, to allow for the widely varying ability in most classrooms. Many activities can be made easier or more challenging by masking and substituting some of the numbers. You may wish to re-use some pages by copying them onto card and laminating them, or by enlarging them onto A3 paper.

Teachers' notes

Brief notes are provided at the foot of each page giving ideas and suggestions for maximising the effectiveness of the activity sheets. These can be masked before copying.

Calculation strategies

Children in Reception year may use the following strategies when working out additions.

Count all Children count each set in ones, then find the total by re-counting from one. For example, 2 + 5 would be said as *one, two* followed by *one, two, three, four, five*; the total is then *one, two, three, four, five, six, seven*.

Count on Children count on from either the first number or the larger number to find the total. For example, 2 + 5 would be said as *two, three, four, five, six, seven* (counting from the first number) or *five, six, seven* (counting from the larger number).

Quick recall Children have enough experience to remember or quickly work out additions; answers are given fairly rapidly.

When working out subtractions, children may use the following strategies.

Count all Children count each set in ones. For example, 5 – 2 would be said as *one, two, three, four, five* followed by what is being taken away: *one, two*. The remainder is then *one, two, three*.

Count back Children count back to find the answer. For example, 5 – 2 would be said as *five, four, three*.

Quick recall Children have enough experience to remember or quickly work out subtractions; answers are given fairly rapidly.

During Reception year, children should move from the count all strategy towards quick recall strategies. Teachers should observe the strategies used by children when completing the activities and steer them towards using mental strategies rather than relying on counting aids such as counters or number lines.

Whole-class warm-up activities

The following activities provide some practical ideas which can be used to introduce the main teaching part of the lesson.

Counting cubes

Allow the children to use interlocking cubes (or other unit apparatus) to practise adding, subtracting and partitioning. Ask questions such as:

- *Pick up four cubes. Now pick up three more. How many altogether?*
- *I have four cubes. You have two more than me. How many do you have? Show me.*
- *You have five cubes. I have three cubes. What questions could we ask?*
- *Pick up seven cubes. Take away three of them. How many are left?*
- *Pick up six cubes. How many must you take away to leave two?*

- *I have five cubes. You have two fewer than me. How many do you have? Show me.*
- *Pick up eight cubes. Put them into two groups/ four groups/equal groups. How many in each group?*

Encourage the children to explain what they have done using the vocabulary of addition.

Number rod swap

Involve the children in adding and subtracting using number rods, which requires them to match rods of equivalent value rather than counting in ones. When subtracting, explain to the children that they cannot simply 'take away'; they must first swap the rod for smaller ones of equivalent value. Ask questions such as:

- *Put together a four-rod and a three-rod. Which rod is the same as this?*
- *Find two rods to match this eight-rod.*
- *Find different pairs of rods to match this ten-rod. Can you put the pairs in order?*
- *Pick up a six-rod. Which swaps will allow you to give me a two-rod? Which swaps will not allow you to give me a two-rod?*
- *Pick up a seven-rod and a four-rod. What is the difference between the rods?*

Show me

Provide each child with a set of 0 to 10 number cards, which they should lay face up in front of them for quick and easy access. Say a calculation, for example *3 plus 2*. Clap your hands three times to allow the children time to work out the answer mentally. Immediately after the last clap, the children hold up the number card showing the answer. Over the course of the year, gradually reduce the time between claps to decrease the thinking time.

What is the question?

Write a number on the board, such as 7, and explain that this is the answer to a calculation. Ask children to come to the board and write calculations which have the answer 7, for example 6 + 1. Encourage them to find a range of additions and subtractions.

1 more

- **Write the numbers.**

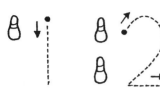 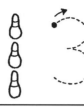 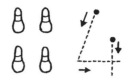 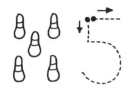

- **Draw** | I more |.

- **Write how many.**

 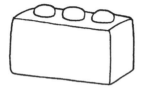  bricks

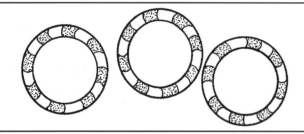  hoops

  cones

- **Draw some balls.**

- **Write how many.**

- **Draw** | I more |.

- **How many now?**

Teachers' note Children should be able to say immediately the number that is one more than a given number. They can use a number line to check if necessary. Once the children are confident with the numbers 1 to 10, gradually increase the range.

Developing Numeracy
Calculations Year R
© A & C Black

Dots

- **Write the numbers.**

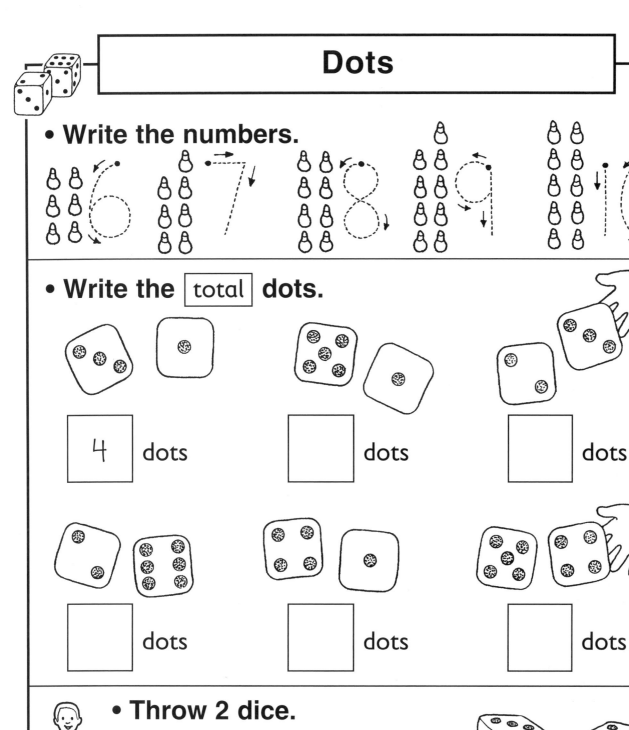

- **Write the** [total] **dots.**

4 dots

[ ] dots

[ ] dots

[ ] dots

[ ] dots

[ ] dots

- **Throw 2 dice.**
- **Draw the dots.**
- **Write the** [total] **dots.**

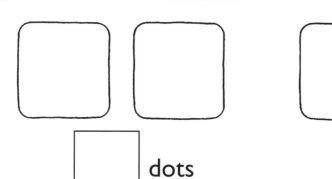

[ ] dots

[ ] dots

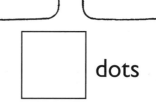

Teachers' note Introduce or revise 'total'. Encourage the children to find totals of small numbers immediately, without always counting in ones. Before beginning the activity, you could sit the children in a circle, each holding a number card in the 1 to 6 range. Roll a large dice: any child with a number card which matches the number of dots on the dice should hold it up.

**Developing Numeracy
Calculations Year R
© A & C Black**

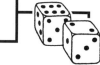

Counting conkers

- **Write how many conkers.**
- **Join the matching pairs.**
- **Ring the odd one out.**

10

10

- **Draw conkers**

  to match the

  odd one out.
- **Write how many.**

Now try this!

Teachers' note Ensure that the children understand the idea of finding the 'odd one out'. Allow the children to play dominoes and number snap, both of which involve finding matching totals.

**Developing Numeracy
Calculations Year R
© A & C Black**

8

Fly the flags

- **Make the strings have** the same number **of flags.**
- **Draw the extra flags on the bottom string.**
- **Write how many you drew.**

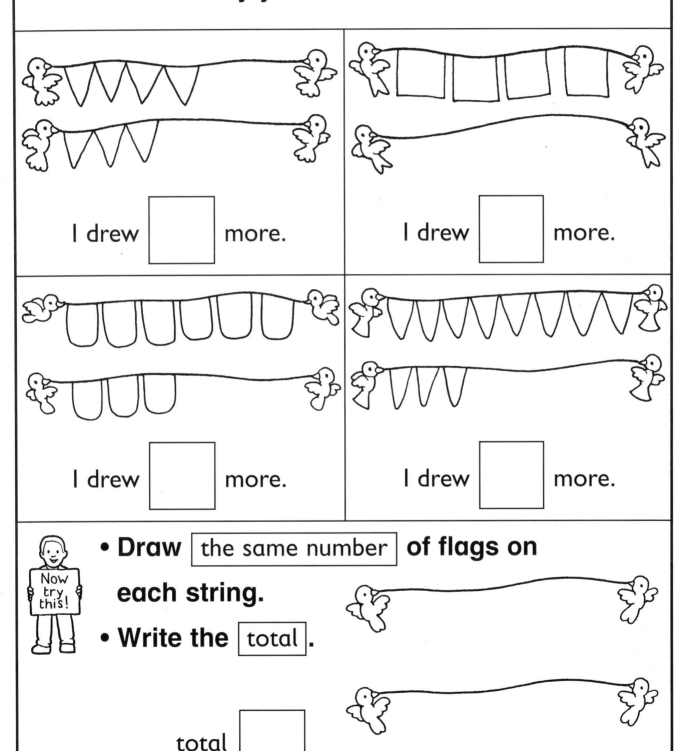

I drew ☐ more.

I drew ☐ more.

I drew ☐ more.

I drew ☐ more.

Now try this!

- **Draw** the same number **of flags on each string.**
- **Write the** total.

total ☐

Teachers' note Some children may find it helpful to do this practically using beads and laces. Ensure that the children are able to count on from different numbers, without always starting at one.

Developing Numeracy Calculations Year R © A & C Black

Dominoes

- **Write the** [total] **dots.**
- **Ring the odd one out.**

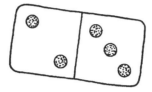
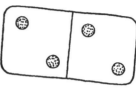
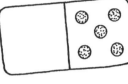

| 5 | | | |

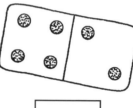
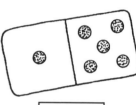

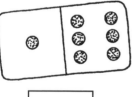
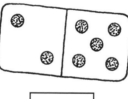
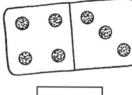
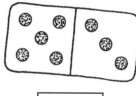

- **Draw spots on the dominoes.**

  Make them have the same [total].

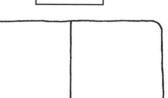

Teachers' note Ensure that the children understand the idea of finding the 'odd one out'. You could introduce the concept using a large set of dominoes. As a further extension, give a group of children a set of dominoes and ask them to find pairs which have the same total.

**Developing Numeracy
Calculations Year R
© A & C Black**

Iceberg game

- **Play with a partner.**

- **Roll a dice. Move your counter.**

Teachers' note Each pair of children needs one copy of the sheet, a dice and two counters in different colours. Alternatively, the children could play in larger groups. Ensure the children understand that they should count the number of jumps along the path.

**Developing Numeracy
Calculations Year R
© A & C Black**

11

Pizza puzzles

- **Write how many mushrooms on each side.**

- **Write how many** $\boxed{\text{altogether}}$ **.**

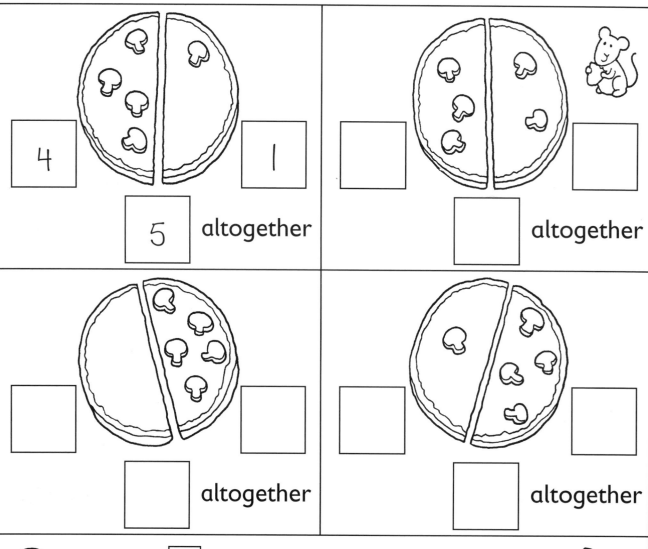

| 4 | | 1 |
| 5 | altogether | |

| | | |
| | altogether | |

| | | |
| | altogether | |

| | | |
| | altogether | |

Now try this!

- **Draw** $\boxed{5}$ **mushrooms.**

- **Write how many in each part.**

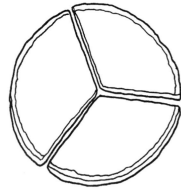

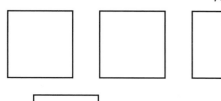

| | | |
| | altogether |

Teachers' note Provide the children with plenty of opportunities to separate (partition) a given number of objects into two groups in a practical play situation, such as in a café or shop. This activity provides practice in partitioning five. Some children may find it hard to recognise zero as a set; you could demonstrate this practically before beginning the activity.

**Developing Numeracy
Calculations Year R
© A & C Black**

The store cupboard

- **Write how many tins on each side.**
- **Write how many** `altogether` .

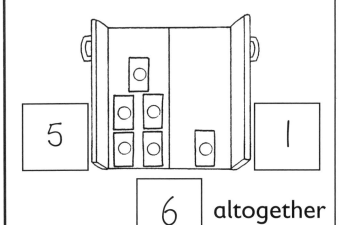

5   1

6   altogether

altogether

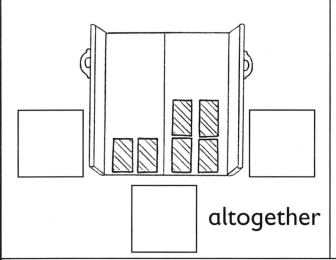

altogether

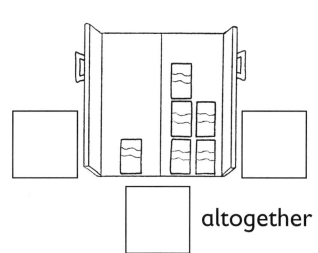

altogether

- **Draw** `6` **tins.**
- **Write how many in each part.**
- **How many** `altogether` **?**

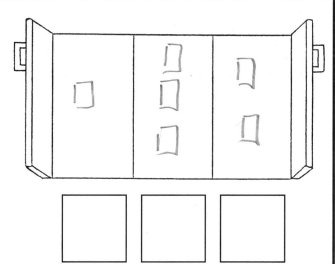

Teachers' note Provide the children with plenty of opportunities to separate (partition) a given number of objects into two groups in a practical play situation, such as in a café or shop. This activity provides practice in partitioning six. Some children may find it hard to recognise zero as a set; you could demonstrate this practically before beginning the activity.

Developing Numeracy
Calculations Year R
© A & C Black

107 June

Paintbrushes

- **Write how many paintbrushes in each pot.**
- **Write how many** | altogether | .

4 3

7 altogether

altogether

altogether

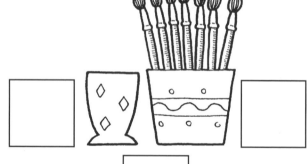

altogether

Now try this!

- **Draw** 7 **paintbrushes.**
- **Write how many**

  in each pot.

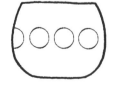

- **How many** | altogether | **?**

Teachers' note Provide the children with plenty of opportunities to separate (partition) a given number of objects into two groups in a practical play situation, such as in a café or shop. This activity provides practice in partitioning seven. Some children may find it hard to recognise zero as a set; you could demonstrate this practically before beginning the activity.

**Developing Numeracy
Calculations Year R
© A & C Black**

14

Baking day

- Draw ⬚8⬚ currants on each bun.
- Write how many on each side.

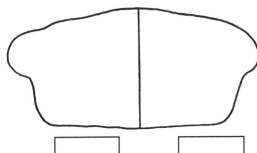

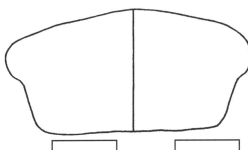

8 is ⬚ and ⬚

8 is ⬚ and ⬚

- Draw ⬚9⬚ candles on each cake.
- Write how many on each side.

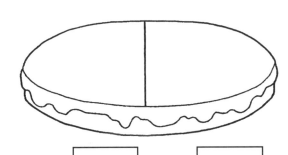

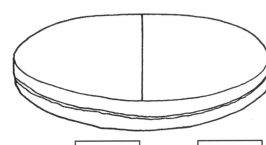

9 is ⬚ and ⬚

9 is ⬚ and ⬚

Now try this!

- Draw ⬚9⬚ candles. Write how many in each part.

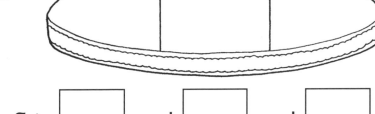

9 is ⬚ and ⬚ and ⬚

Teachers' note This activity provides practice in partitioning eight and nine. The children could do the activity practically using counters. Discuss the different answers that children offer and whether the same number can be on each side. For the extension activity, ask whether anyone has drawn the same number of candles in each part.

**Developing Numeracy
Calculations Year R
© A & C Black**

Spotty shirts

- **Draw** 10 **spots on each T-shirt.**
- **Write how many on each side.**

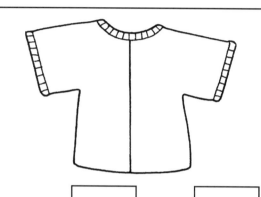

10 is ☐ and ☐

10 is ☐ and ☐

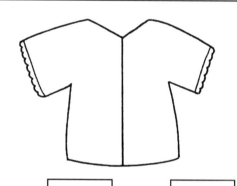

10 is ☐ and ☐

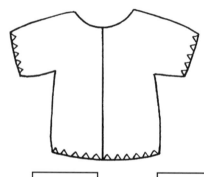

10 is ☐ and ☐

Now try this!

- **Draw** 10 **spots on the scarf.**
- **Write how many in each part.**

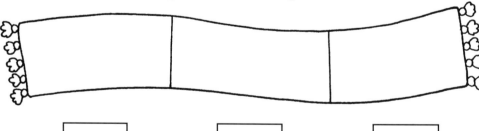

10 is ☐ and ☐ and ☐

Teachers' note This activity provides practice in partitioning ten. The children could do the activity practically using counters. Discuss the different answers that children offer and whether the same number can be on each side.

**Developing Numeracy
Calculations Year R
© A & C Black**

Ladybirds

Teachers' note Provide one copy of the sheet for each pair of children. Cut out the cards. The children should use pairs of cards to make whole ladybirds. Ask questions such as: 'Which ladybirds have the same number of spots on each side?' 'Which has the largest total?' The children could make several ladybirds with the same total. Discuss ladybirds with totals of more than ten.

**Developing Numeracy
Calculations Year R**
© A & C Black

Add the Mice

• Count and add.

    2 add 2

4 **altogether**

Altogether means add the numbers.

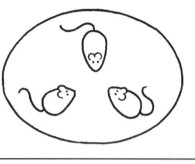 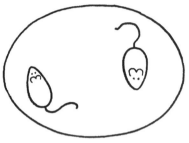   add

altogether

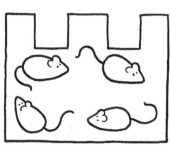 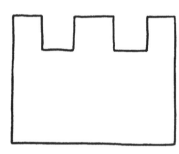   add

altogether

    add

altogether

• Draw ⬜5 **mice.**

 Now try this!

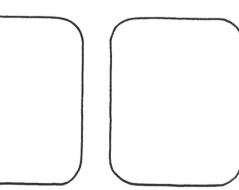   add

altogether

Teachers' note This activity provides practice in making totals of five or less. Introduce or revise 'add' and 'altogether'. If appropriate, discuss other language associated with addition. Some children may find it helpful to use counters to represent the mice.

**Developing Numeracy
Calculations Year R
© A & C Black**

18

Make 10

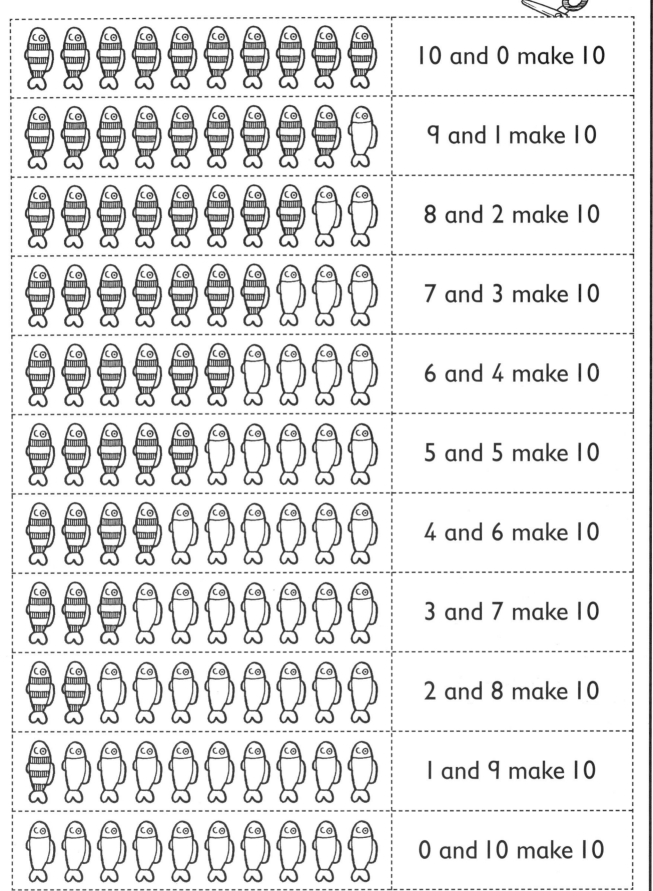

	10 and 0 make 10
	9 and 1 make 10
	8 and 2 make 10
	7 and 3 make 10
	6 and 4 make 10
	5 and 5 make 10
	4 and 6 make 10
	3 and 7 make 10
	2 and 8 make 10
	1 and 9 make 10
	0 and 10 make 10

Addition puzzles

• **Write the additions.**

+ means **add**.
= means **equals** or
is the same as.

2	+	3	=	5

	+		=	

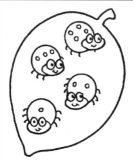

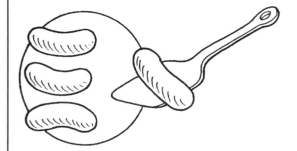

	+		=	

	+		=	

	+		=	

	+		=	

• **Write 2 more additions.**

Make the answer equal 5 .

Teachers' note Introduce or revise 'addition' and the plus and equals signs. Some children may find it helpful to use counters to represent the objects in the pictures.

Developing Numeracy
Calculations Year R
© A & C Black

Eye spy

- **Draw** $\boxed{6}$ **eyes on each alien.**

Use + and =.

- **Write the addition.**

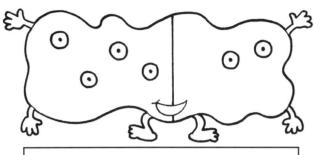

$4 + 2 = 6$

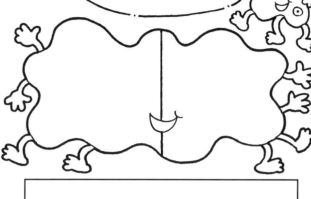

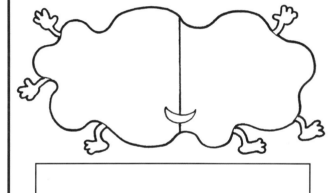

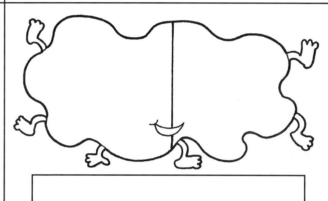

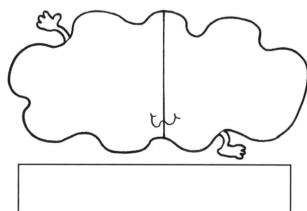

Now try this!

- **Write pairs of numbers that add up to** $\boxed{6}$.

0 and 6

_____

_____

Teachers' note Ask the children to make each addition different. Ensure they realise that the order of adding does not matter (for example, 2 + 4 has the same answer as 4 + 2). Some children may find it helpful to use six counters as an aid. For the extension activity, encourage the children to write the number pairs in order.

**Developing Numeracy
Calculations Year R
© A & C Black**

21

Butterfly spots

- **Draw** 7 **spots on each butterfly.**

- **Write the addition.** Use + and =.

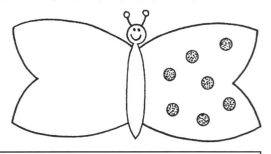

0 + 7 = 7

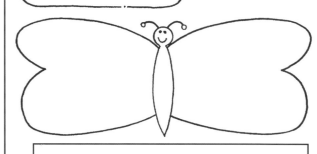

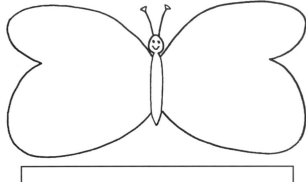

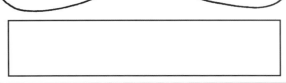

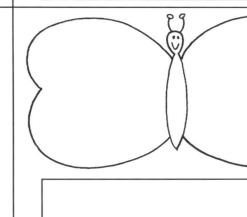

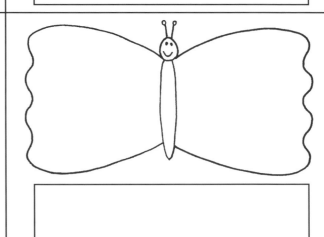

 Now try this!

- **Write pairs of numbers that add up to** 7 .

0 and 7 _____

_____ _____

Teachers' note Ask the children to make each addition different. Ensure they realise that the order of adding does not matter (for example, 0 + 7 has the same answer as 7 + 0). Some children may find it helpful to use seven counters as an aid. For the extension activity, encourage the children to write the number pairs in order.

**Developing Numeracy
Calculations Year R
© A & C Black**

Snapping crocodiles

- **Draw** 8 **teeth on each crocodile.**

- **Write the addition.**

Use + and =.

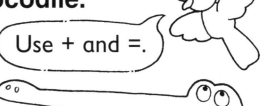

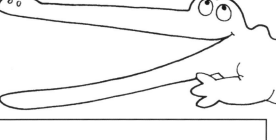

5 + 3 = 8

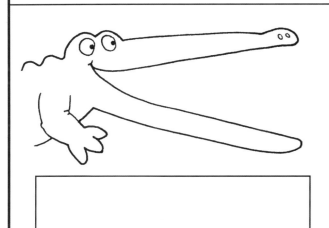

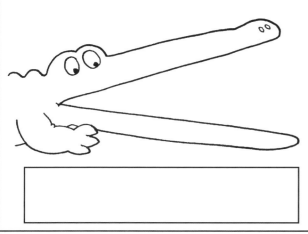

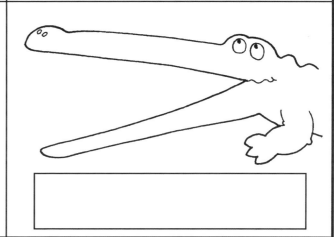

- **Write pairs of numbers that add up to** 8 .

0 and 8 _____ _____

_____ _____

Teachers' note Ask the children to make each addition different. Ensure they realise that the order of adding does not matter (for example, 3 + 5 has the same answer as 5 + 3). Some children may find it helpful to use eight counters as an aid. For the extension activity, encourage the children to write the number pairs in order.

**Developing Numeracy
Calculations Year R
© A & C Black**

Rainy day

• Draw [9] raindrops on each window.

• **Write the addition.**

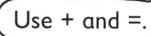
Use + and =.

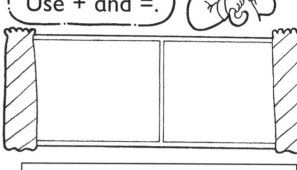

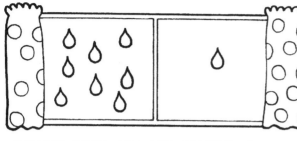

$$8 + 1 = 9$$

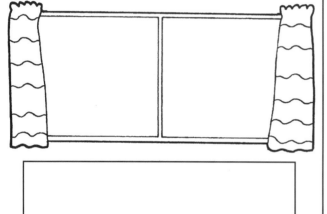

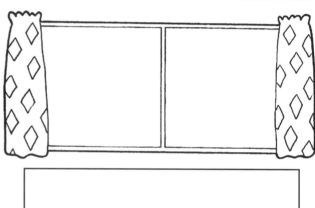

Now try this!

• **Write pairs of numbers that add up to [9].**

0 and 9 _____ _____

_____ _____

Teachers' note Ask the children to make each addition different. Ensure they realise that the order of adding does not matter (for example, 1 + 8 has the same answer as 8 + 1). Some children may find it helpful to use nine counters as an aid. For the extension activity, encourage the children to write the number pairs in order.

**Developing Numeracy
Calculations Year R
© A & C Black**

Centipedes

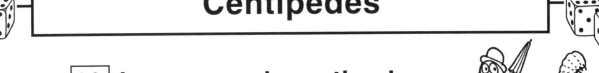

- Draw 10 legs on each centipede.

- Write the addition.

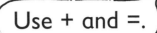
Use + and =.

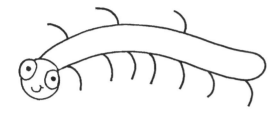

$3 + 7 = 10$

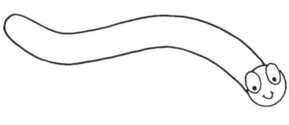

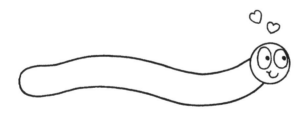

Now try this!

- Write pairs of numbers that add up to 10.

0 and 10 _____ _____

_____ _____ _____

Teachers' note Ask the children to make each addition different. Ensure they realise that the order of adding does not matter (for example, 3 + 7 has the same answer as 7 + 3). Some children may find it helpful to use ten counters as an aid. For the extension activity, encourage the children to write the number pairs in order.

Developing Numeracy
Calculations Year R
© A & C Black

Double trouble

- **Look at these** doubles.

- **Write the additions.**

Doubling is adding a number to itself.

| 3 | + | 3 | = | 6 |

☐ + ☐ = ☐

☐ + ☐ = ☐

☐ + ☐ = ☐

☐ + ☐ = ☐

☐ + ☐ = ☐

- **Double each number. Write the addition.**

Now try this!

3

2

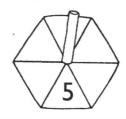
5

Teachers' note Introduce or revise 'double'. The children should begin to know by heart the doubles of all numbers up to about five. You could use the 'Show me' activity on page 5 to practise finding doubles using quick recall.

**Developing Numeracy
Calculations Year R
© A & C Black**

Jumping squirrel

You can use a number line to help you $\boxed{\text{add}}$.

$1 + 3 =$ 4

Start at 1.

Count 3 jumps.

The answer is 4.

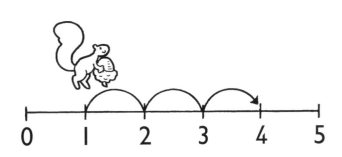

• **Write the answers.**

Count the jumps and write where you land!

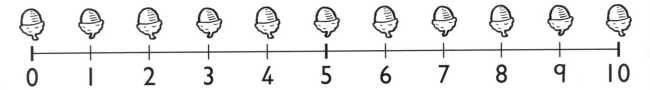

$4 + 2 =$

$1 + 4 =$

$6 + 3 =$

$5 + 5 =$

$0 + 7 =$

$2 + 3 =$

• **Write the missing numbers.**

$3 + = 7$

$ + 1 = 9$

$ + = 10$

Teachers' note Revise the plus and equals signs and check that the children count the number of jumps on the number line. Using a number line is a progression from using counters, but it is important that children do not become over-reliant on this strategy. Number lines should be seen as a stepping stone towards mental strategies such as counting on and quick recall.

Developing Numeracy Calculations Year R © A & C Black

Quick jumps

When you add, start at the larger number.

2 + 7 = 9

Start at 7.

Count 2 jumps.

The answer is 9.

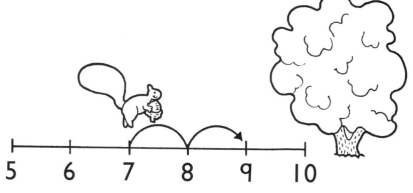

- ## Choose which number to start at.

- ## Write the answers.

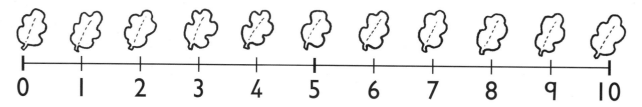

6 + 2 =

3 + 7 =

1 + 8 =

0 + 4 =

2 + 6 =

5 + 2 =

- ## Start at 2.

- ## Make 2 jumps to land on 10.

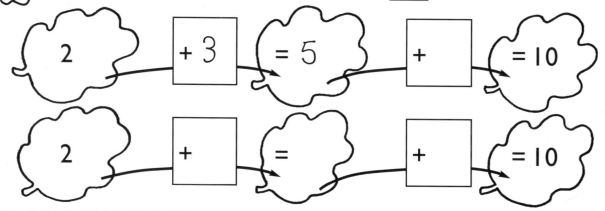

2   + 3   = 5   +   = 10

2   +   =   +   = 10

Teachers' note The children should first complete the activity on page 27. Discuss that the order of adding does not matter (for example, 2 + 7 has the same answer as 7 + 2). Number rods are particularly useful for showing this. For the extension activity, reassure the children that the two jumps do not have to be of the same value.

Developing Numeracy
Calculations Year R
© A & C Black

Saving pennies

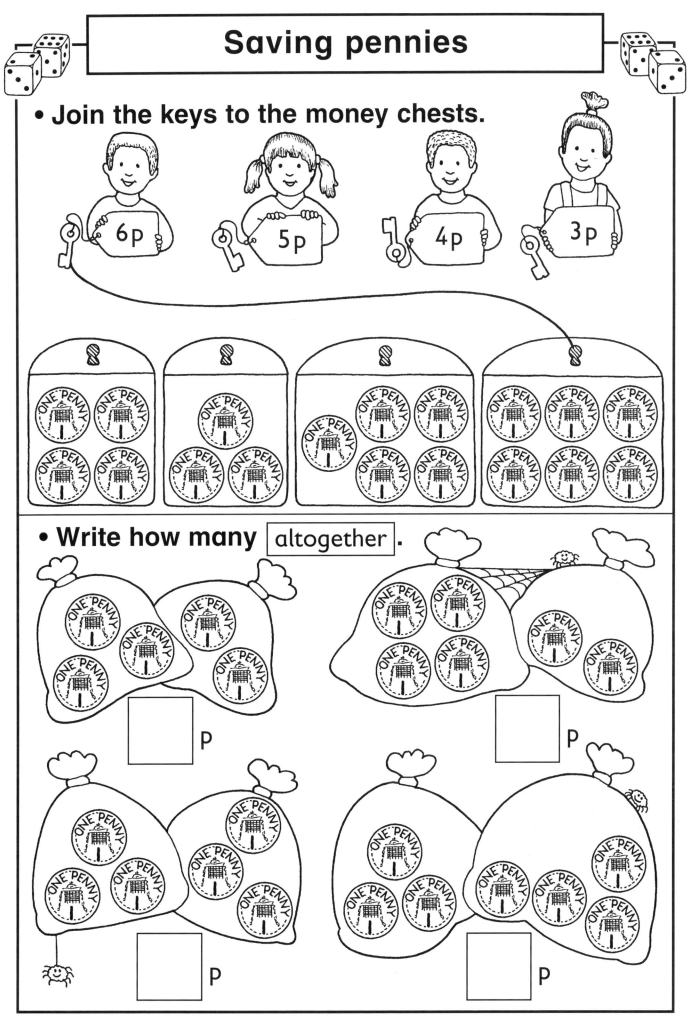

- **Join the keys to the money chests.**

6p   5p   4p   3p

- **Write how many** altogether .

☐ P

☐ P

☐ P

☐ P

Teachers' note If necessary, revise 'altogether'. Ensure that the children are familiar with the 1p coin. Some children may find it helpful to use real 1p coins as an aid. Encourage them to recognise the number of coins without having to count them individually. In the second part of the activity, the children should count on from the largest set of coins.

Developing Numeracy Calculations Year R © A & C Black

Rich piggies

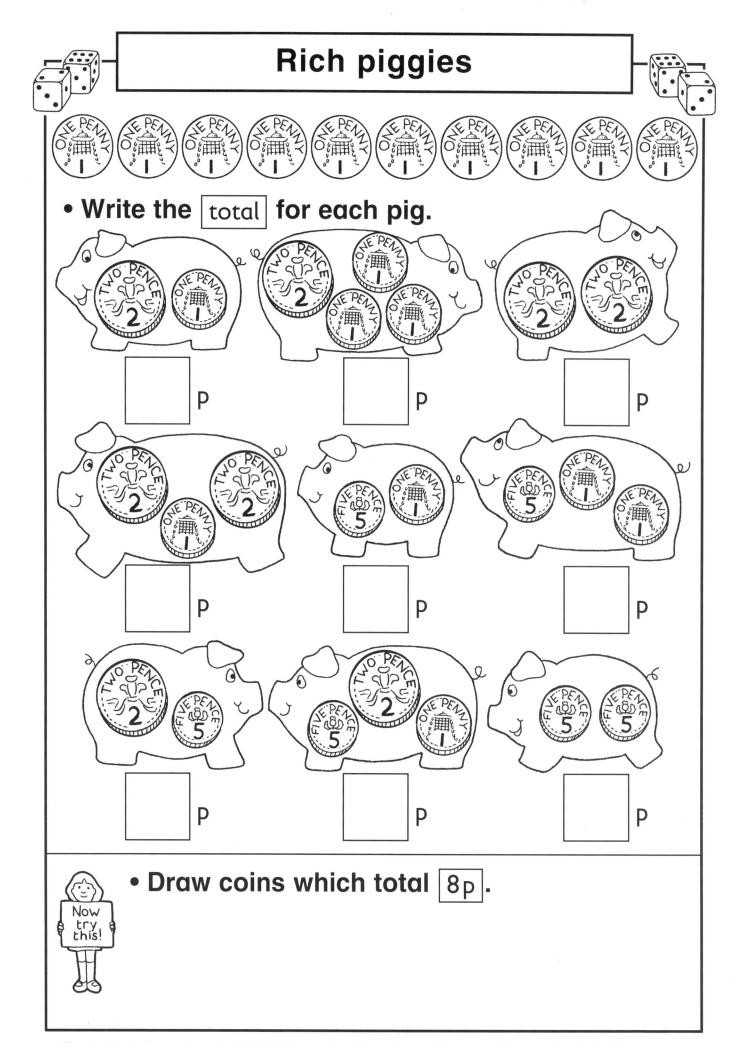

• Write the ⬚total⬚ for each pig.

• Draw coins which total ⬚8 p⬚.

Developing Numeracy
Calculations Year R
© A & C Black

Teachers' note If necessary, revise 'total'. Children may benefit from using real coins as an aid. Some children may need to exchange 2p and 5p coins for 1p coins. The coin track at the top of the sheet can be used as an aid. For the extension activity, the children could use rubber stamps or rubbings.

To the rescue!

0 1 2 3 4 5 6 7 8 9 10 11 12

☆ Roll 2 dice.

☆ Add the numbers.

$3 + 4 = 7$

☆ Colour a rung on the matching ladder.

7

☆ Which knight reaches the princess first?

You need 2 dice and a coloured pencil.

1 2 3 4 5 6 7 8 9 10 11 12

Teachers' note The children may need to use the number line when adding the numbers. Encourage them to guess which knight will reach the princess, i.e. which score will occur most frequently. The game can be played with two children each choosing a ladder as theirs. The winner is the first to the top. Ask the children why a score of one will never occur when rolling two dice.

Developing Numeracy Calculations Year R
© A & C Black

Road maze

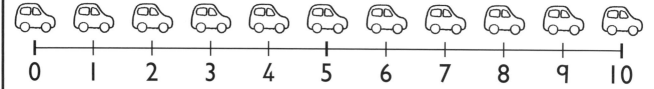

0 1 2 3 4 5 6 7 8 9 10

- **Follow the paths.**

- **Write the answers on the bus stops.**

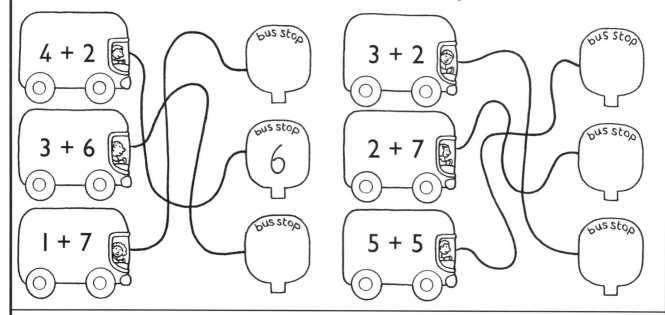

4 + 2

3 + 6

1 + 7

3 + 2

2 + 7

5 + 5

bus stop

bus stop 6

bus stop

bus stop

bus stop

bus stop

- **Join each car to the right answer.**
  Use your finger, then use a pencil.

Now try this!

2 + 2

3 + 3

4 + 4

5 + 5

6

4

10

8

Use a different colour for each car.

Teachers' note Before beginning the activity, introduce or revise doubles. Some children may not need to use the number line; it could be masked if appropriate.

**Developing Numeracy
Calculations Year R
© A & C Black**

Stop thief!

Magpie takes ☐ 1 jewel from each pot.

• Write the total and how many are left.

| 3 | I less ➤ | 2 | left |

| ☐ | I less ➤ | ☐ | left |

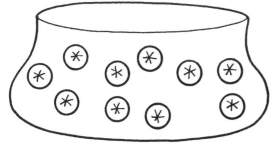

| ☐ | I less ➤ | ☐ | left |

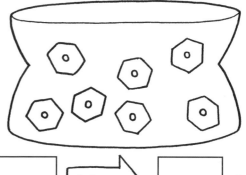

| ☐ | I less ➤ | ☐ | left |

 Now try this!

• Draw some jewels. Write how many.

• Draw and write how many are left.

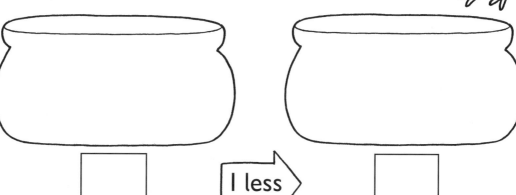

| ☐ | I less ➤ | ☐ |

Teachers' note The children may find it helpful to cross off a jewel in each pot, or to cover it with a counter. Discuss with the children that there will be fewer jewels after Magpie visits. As a further extension, ask how many jewels would be left if Magpie took two from each pot.

Developing Numeracy
Calculations Year R
© A & C Black

33

Musical chairs

- **Start with** 5 **chairs each time.**
- **Draw and write how many are left.**

5  take away 3 → 2 left

5 take away 2 → ☐ left

5 take away 4 → ☐ left

5 take away 1 → ☐ left

 • **Write the missing numbers.**

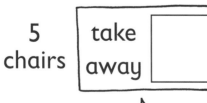

5 chairs take away ☐ → 2 left

5 chairs take away ☐ → 0 left

5 chairs take away ☐ → 5 left

Teachers' note Ensure that the children know all the subtractions from five, including those which involve zero. Explain that the worked example shows the number of chairs left, not the number started with.

Developing Numeracy Calculations Year R © A & C Black

34

Yummy eggs

- **Start with** 6 **eggs each time.**
- **Draw and write how many are left.**

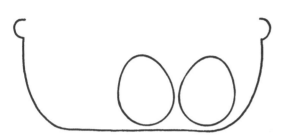

6 **take away 4** → 2 left

6 **take away 5** → [ ] left

6 **take away 3** → [ ] left

6 **take away 2** → [ ] left

- **Write the missing numbers.**

Now try this!

6 eggs **take away** [ ] → 1 left

6 eggs **take away** [ ] → 0 left

6 eggs **take away** [ ] → 6 left

Teachers' note Ensure that the children know all the subtractions from six, including those which involve zero. Explain that the worked example shows the number of eggs left, not the number started with.

**Developing Numeracy
Calculations Year R
© A & C Black**

Fish for Mog

- **Start with** $\boxed{7}$ **fish each time.**
- **Draw and write how many are left.**

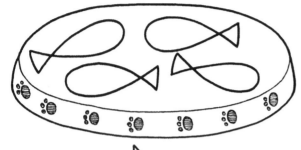

7 [take away 3] → 4 left

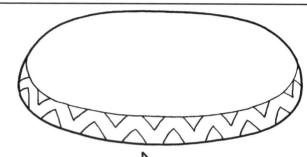

7 [take away 6] → ☐ left

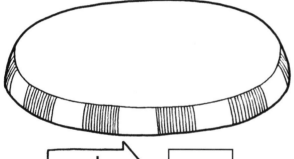

7 [take away 5] → ☐ left

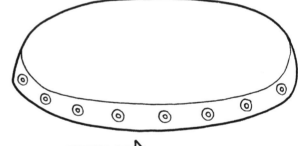

7 [take away 4] → ☐ left

- **Write the missing numbers.**

7 fish [take away ☐] → 2 left

7 fish [take away ☐] → 0 left

7 fish [take away ☐] → 7 left

Teachers' note Ensure that the children know all the subtractions from seven, including those which involve zero. Explain that the worked example shows the number of fish left, not the number started with.

**Developing Numeracy
Calculations Year R**
© A & C Black

Doggy treats

- **Start with** 8 **bones each time.**
- **Write how many are left.**

8 take away 4 — 4 left

8 take away 1 — left

8 take away 2 — left

8 take away 3 — left

8 take away 5 — left

8 take away 6 — left

- **Write the missing numbers.**

8 bones | take away [ ] | 8 left

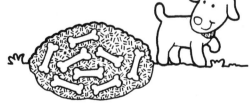

8 bones | take away [ ] | 0 left

8 bones | take away [ ] | 1 left

Teachers' note Ensure that the children know all the subtractions from eight, including those which involve zero.

**Developing Numeracy
Calculations Year R
© A & C Black**

Run, rabbit, run!

- **Start with** $\boxed{9}$ **carrots each time.**
- **Write how many are left.**

9   take away 4   5 left

9   take away 2   left

9   take away 7   left

9   take away 3   left

9   take away 5   left

9   take away 6   left

- **Write the missing numbers.**

Now try this!

9 carrots   take away ☐   9 left

9 carrots   take away ☐   0 left

9 carrots   take away ☐   1 left

Teachers' note Ensure that the children know all the subtractions from nine, including those which involve zero.

Developing Numeracy
Calculations Year R
© A & C Black

Go bananas!

- **Start with ▢10 bananas each time.**
- **Write how many are left.**

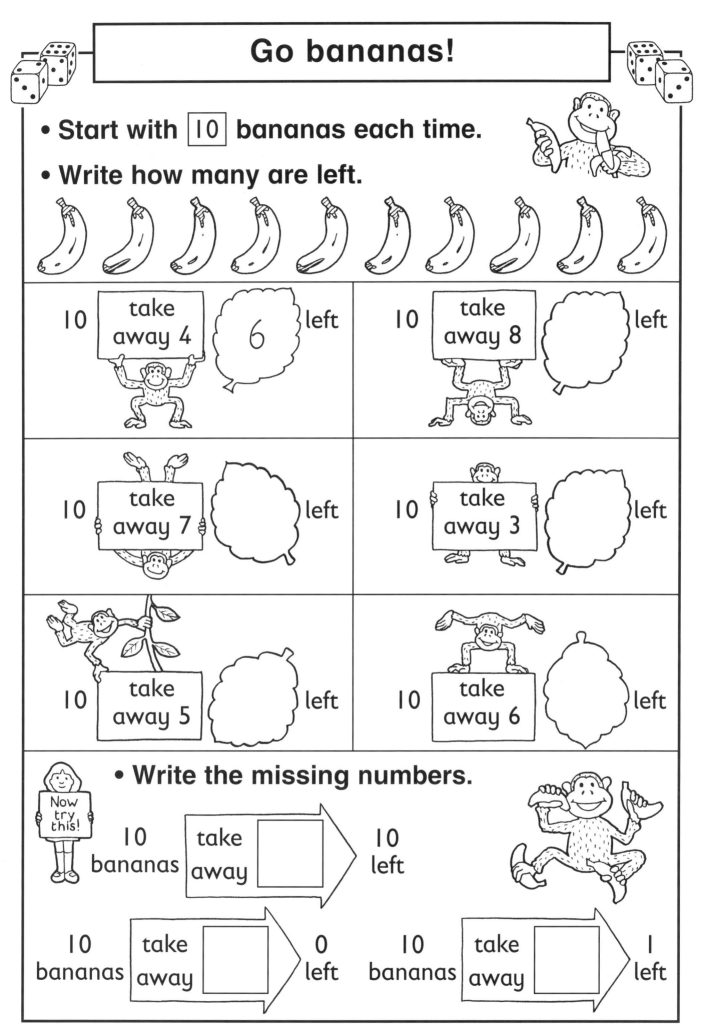

10 take away 4 — 6 left

10 take away 8 — left

10 take away 7 — left

10 take away 3 — left

10 take away 5 — left

10 take away 6 — left

- **Write the missing numbers.**

Now try this!

10 bananas take away ▢ → 10 left

10 bananas take away ▢ → 0 left

10 bananas take away ▢ → 1 left

Teachers' note Ensure that the children know all the subtractions from ten, including those which involve zero.

Developing Numeracy
Calculations Year R
© A & C Black

Fruit snacks

- Start with ⏧10⏧ pennies each time.

- Pay for the fruit.

- Write how much is left.

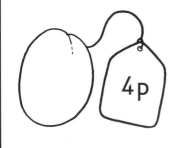 | 6 | p left

 | ☐ | p left

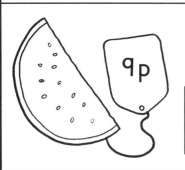 | ☐ | p left

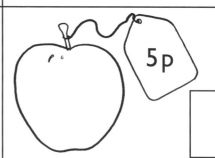 | ☐ | p left

 | ☐ | p left

 | ☐ | p left

Dean had ⏧10⏧ pennies.

He has ⏧4⏧ pennies left.

- Write how much he spent. ☐ p

Teachers' note The children may find it helpful to use the coin track at the top of the sheet and real 1p coins as an aid. Encourage them to use the language of subtraction in practical play situations, such as in a café or shop.

Developing Numeracy
Calculations Year R
© A & C Black

Flies for dinner!

• **How many flies are left? Write and draw.**

I eat 3.

7 left

I eat 4.

☐ left

I eat 2.

☐ left

I eat 5.

☐ left

I eat 4.

☐ left

• **Draw some flies.**

• **Draw and write how many are left.**

I eat ☐ .

☐ left

Teachers' note The children may find it helpful to cross off the flies that are eaten. They could use counters to represent the flies.

**Developing Numeracy
Calculations Year R
© A & C Black**

Wanda the witch

- **Write how many in each row.**

- **Write the** [difference] **.**

Count on from the smaller number to the larger.

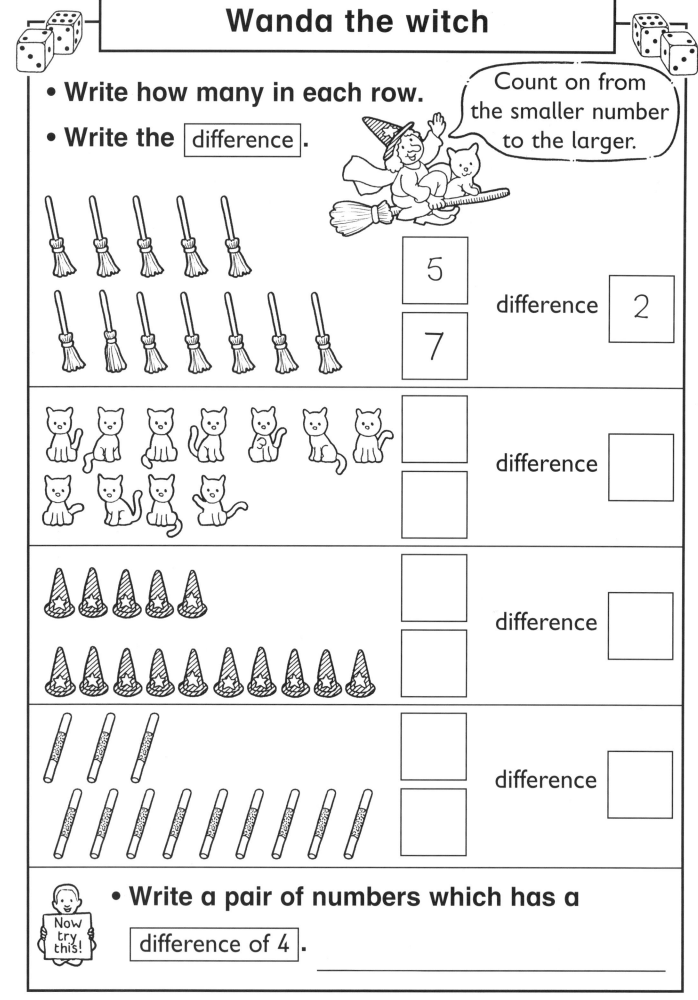

5
7

difference 2

difference

difference

difference

- **Write a pair of numbers which has a**

[difference of 4] . _____

Teachers' note Introduce 'difference'. If children have difficulty with the term, it can help to talk about 'number difference' to distinguish it from other differences such as colour or size. For the extension activity, the children can find the pairs by counting on four from their chosen first number. The ladybird cards on page 17 can be used to find a difference of one spot, two spots and so on.

Developing Numeracy Calculations Year R © A & C Black

Tree jumps

- **Move a counter down the tree to find the missing numbers.**

10	
9	Start on 5. Jump back 2. Land on 3 .
8	
7	Start on 8. Jump back 3. Land on .
6	Start on 4. Jump back 4. Land on .
5	
4	Start on 6. Jump back 5. Land on .
3	Start on 9. Jump back 3. Land on .
2	
1	Start on 7. Jump back 4. Land on .
0	

- **Write numbers on the leaves.**

Now try this!

Start on 8. Jump back ⬭ . Land on ⬭ .

Start on 5. Jump back ⬭ . Land on ⬭ .

Teachers' note Each child needs a counter to move along the tree. Encourage children to estimate where the counter will land before they move it.

Developing Numeracy
Calculations Year R
© A & C Black

Pin cushions

- **Draw the pins.**
- **Write the missing numbers.**

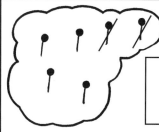 **6** take away 2 leaves **4**

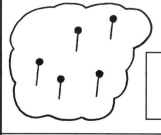 take away 3 leaves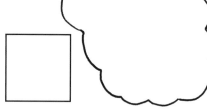

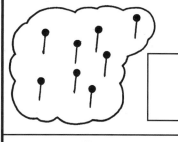 subtract 5 leaves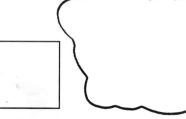

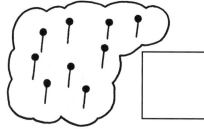 subtract 2 leaves

- **Write the missing numbers.**

6 take away 4 leaves

10 subtract 3 leaves

Teachers' note The children may find it helpful to cross off the objects that are taken away. They could use counters to represent the pins.

Developing Numeracy Calculations Year R © A & C Black

Jack and Jill game

- **Play with a partner.**
- **Roll a dice. Move your counter.**

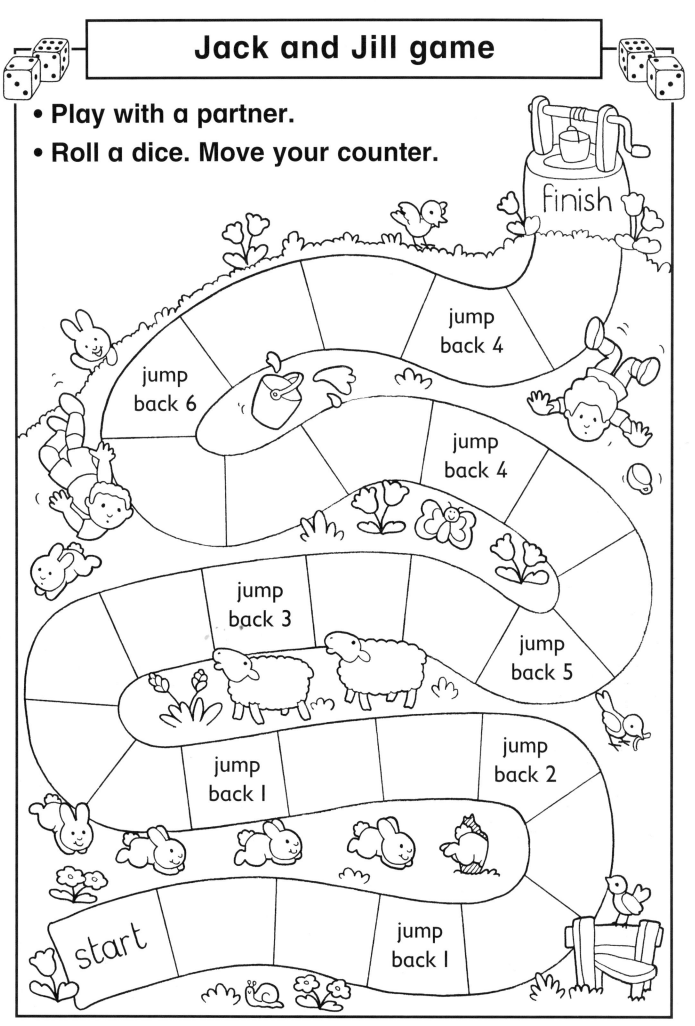

finish

jump back 4

jump back 6

jump back 4

jump back 3

jump back 5

jump back 1

jump back 2

start

jump back 1

jump back 1

Teachers' note Each pair of children needs a copy of the sheet, a dice and two counters in different colours. You could photocopy the page onto A3 paper or card. Ensure the children realise that they should count the number of jumps.

Developing Numeracy
Calculations Year R
© A & C Black

Button box

• **Write the** [substractions] .

– means take away.
= means equals or is the same as.

 take away

$$\boxed{5} - \boxed{2} = \boxed{3}$$

 take away

$$\boxed{} - \boxed{} = \boxed{}$$

 take away

$$\boxed{} - \boxed{} = \boxed{}$$

 take away

$$\boxed{} - \boxed{} = \boxed{}$$

 take away

$$\boxed{} - \boxed{} = \boxed{}$$

• **Use the buttons to help you count.**

• **Write the answers.**

$8 - 3 = \boxed{}$ $8 - 6 = \boxed{}$ $8 - 4 = \boxed{}$

• **Write the answers on the buttons.**

$5 - 5 = \bigcirc$ $3 - 0 = \bigcirc$ $7 - 7 = \bigcirc$

Teachers' note If necessary, revise the minus and equals signs. Some children may need to use real buttons or counters for the first part of the sheet.

**Developing Numeracy
Calculations Year R
© A & C Black**

• **Use a number line to help you** $\boxed{\text{subtract}}$.

$10 - 4 = \text{⟨} 6 \text{⟩}$

Start at 10.

Count back 4 jumps.

The answer is 6.

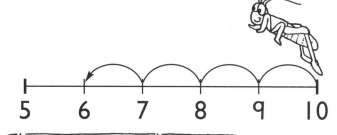

| 5 | 6 | 7 | 8 | 9 | 10 |

Count the jumps and write where you land!

• **Write the answers.**

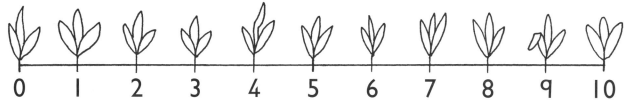

0 1 2 3 4 5 6 7 8 9 10

$7 - 4 =$ ⟨⟩ $9 - 5 =$ ⟨⟩ $5 - 2 =$ ⟨⟩

$6 - 4 =$ ⟨⟩ $8 - 5 =$ ⟨⟩ $10 - 3 =$ ⟨⟩

Now try this!

• **Write the missing numbers.**

$8 - \text{⟨} \text{⟩} = 4$ $6 - \text{⟨} \text{⟩} = 5$

$\text{⟨} \text{⟩} - \text{⟨} \text{⟩} = 3$

Teachers' note If necessary, revise the minus and equals signs. Ensure the children understand that they should count the number of jumps. Reassure them that there are several possible answers for the last extension question.

**Developing Numeracy
Calculations Year R
© A & C Black**

Pet puzzles

0 1 2 3 4 5 6 7 8 9 10

- **Follow the dog leads.**

- **Write the answers on the blocks.**

8 – 2

9 – 5

7 – 1

6

10 – 8

10 – 5

10 – 2

Now try this!

- **Join each hamster to the right bowl.**

  Use your finger, then use a pencil.

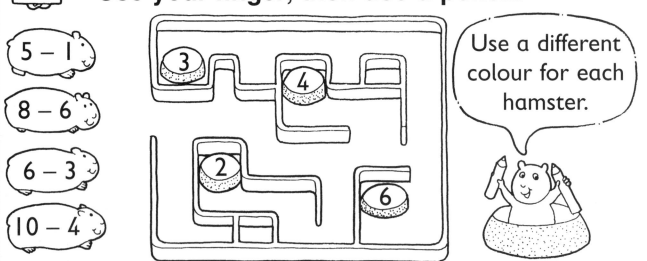

5 – 1

8 – 6

6 – 3

10 – 4

3

4

2

6

Use a different colour for each hamster.

Teachers' note If necessary, revise the minus sign. Some children may not need to use the number line; it could be masked if appropriate. You may wish to mask and substitute the numbers to make the activity easier or more challenging.

**Developing Numeracy
Calculations Year R**
© A & C Black

Picking strawberries

– means take away.

• **Complete the** subtractions .

$$6 - 2 = 4$$

$$\boxed{} - 3 = \boxed{}$$

$$\boxed{} - 9 = \boxed{}$$

$$\boxed{} - 4 = \boxed{}$$

$$\boxed{} - 7 = \boxed{}$$

$$\boxed{} - 0 = \boxed{}$$

Now try this!

• **Start with** 10 **strawberries each time.**

• **Work out how many have been picked.**

$$10 - \boxed{4} = \boxed{6}$$

$$10 - \boxed{} = \boxed{}$$

$$10 - \boxed{} = \boxed{}$$

$$10 - \boxed{} = \boxed{}$$

Teachers' note The children could use counters as an aid. There are often misunderstandings with missing number calculations of the type □ – 3 = 5. Discuss the calculations with the children, making sure they realise that the first number is the starting point ('start number'), the second number is what is being subtracted ('action'), and the third number is the result ('answer').

Developing Numeracy Calculations Year R © A & C Black

49

Rocket launch

The answers are on the rocket.

- **Write the missing numbers.**

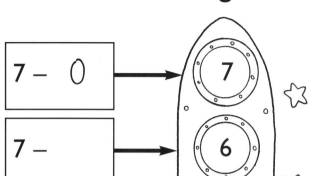

| 7 – 0 | → | 7 |

| 7 – | → | 6 |

| 7 – | → | 5 |

| 7 – | → | 4 |

| 7 – | → | 3 |

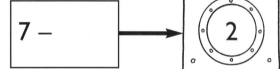

| 7 – | → | 2 |

| 7 – | → | 1 |

| 7 – | → | 0 |

| 7 – 0 | → | 7 |

| – 0 | → | 6 |

| – 0 | → | 5 |

| – 0 | → | 4 |

| – 0 | → | 3 |

| – 0 | → | 2 |

| – 0 | → | 1 |

| – 0 | → | 0 |

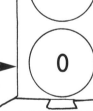

- **Write numbers on the space ships.**

Now try this!

$7 - = $

$7 - = $

Make each subtraction different.

$7 - =$

Teachers' note If necessary, revise the minus and equals signs. The children can use the numbers on the rocket as a number track to help with the subtractions. Counters or number rods can also be used. For the extension activity, ensure the children understand that the subtractions must give the correct answers.

**Developing Numeracy
Calculations Year R
© A & C Black**

Rollercoaster ride

The answers are on the carriages.

• Write the missing numbers.

8 – 0	8
8 –	7
8 –	6
8 –	5
8 –	4
8 –	3
8 –	2
8 –	1
8 –	0

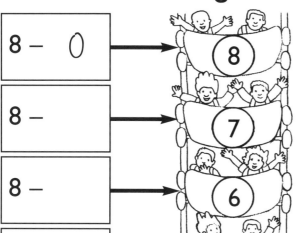
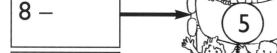

8 – 0	8
– 0	7
– 0	6
– 0	5
– 0	4
– 0	3
– 0	2
– 0	1
– 0	0

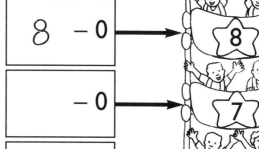

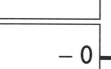

• Write numbers on the carriages.

Now try this!

8 – 〔 〕 = 〔 〕

Make each subtraction different.

8 – 〔 〕 = 〔 〕   8 – 〔 〕 = 〔 〕

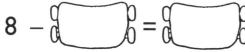

Teachers' note If necessary, revise the minus and equals signs. The children can use the numbers on the rollercoaster as a number track to help with the subtractions. Counters or number rods can also be used. For the extension activity, ensure the children understand that the subtractions must give the correct answers.

**Developing Numeracy
Calculations Year R**
© A & C Black

51

Helter skelter

The answers are on the helter skelter.

• **Write the missing numbers.**

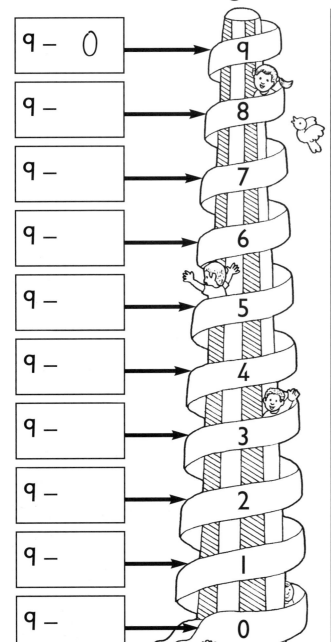

q – 0	→ 9
q –	→ 8
q –	→ 7
q –	→ 6
q –	→ 5
q –	→ 4
q –	→ 3
q –	→ 2
q –	→ 1
q –	→ 0

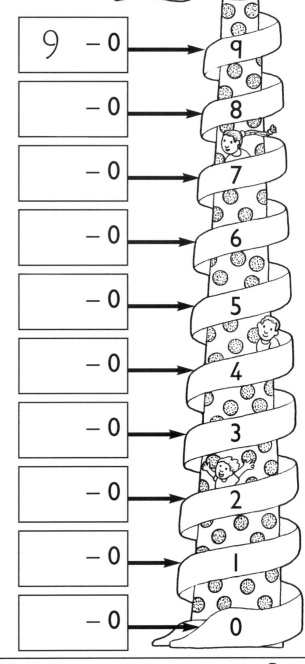

9 – 0	→ 9
– 0	→ 8
– 0	→ 7
– 0	→ 6
– 0	→ 5
– 0	→ 4
– 0	→ 3
– 0	→ 2
– 0	→ 1
– 0	→ 0

Now try this!

• **Write numbers on the mats.**

q – ☐ = ☐

q – ☐ = ☐

Make each subtraction different.

q – ☐ = ☐

Developing Numeracy
Calculations Year R
© A & C Black

Teachers' note If necessary, revise the minus and equals signs. The children can use the numbers on the helter skelter as a number track to help with the subtractions. Counters or number rods can also be used. For the extension activity, ensure the children understand that the subtractions must give the correct answers.

Lighthouses

The answers are on the lighthouse.

• **Write the missing numbers.**

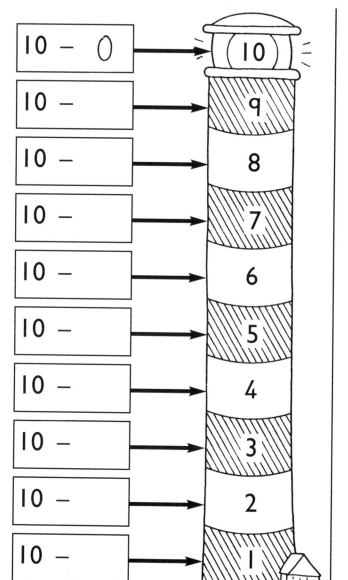

10 − 0	→ 10
10 −	→ 9
10 −	→ 8
10 −	→ 7
10 −	→ 6
10 −	→ 5
10 −	→ 4
10 −	→ 3
10 −	→ 2
10 −	→ 1
10 −	→ 0

10 − 0	→ 10
− 0	→ 9
− 0	→ 8
− 0	→ 7
− 0	→ 6
− 0	→ 5
− 0	→ 4
− 0	→ 3
− 0	→ 2
− 0	→ 1
− 0	→ 0

Now try this!

• **Write numbers on the hats.**

Make each subtraction different.

10 − ⬜ = ⬜

10 − ⬜ = ⬜   10 − ⬜ = ⬜

Teachers' note If necessary, revise the minus and equals signs. The children can use the numbers on the lighthouse as a number track to help with the subtractions. Counters or number rods can also be used. For the extension activity, ensure the children understand that the subtractions must give the correct answers.

**Developing Numeracy
Calculations Year R
© A & C Black**

Footprints

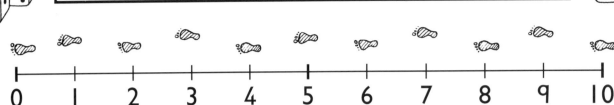

```
0   1   2   3   4   5   6   7   8   9   10
```

• ## Write the missing numbers.

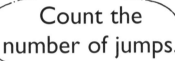
Count the number of jumps.

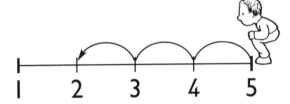

```
1   2   3   4   5
```

$$5 - \boxed{3} = 2$$

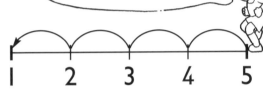

```
1   2   3   4   5
```

$$5 - \boxed{} = 1$$

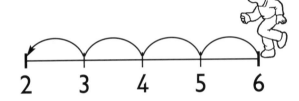

```
2   3   4   5   6
```

$$6 - \boxed{} = 2$$

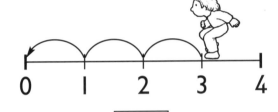

```
0   1   2   3   4
```

$$3 - \boxed{} = 0$$

• ## Join each shoe to its answer on the line.

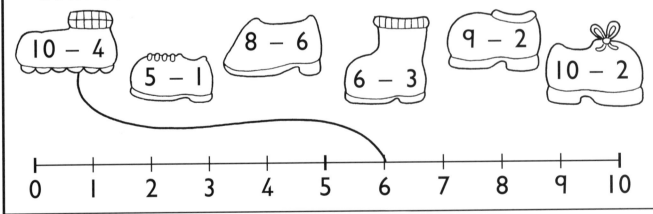

10 – 4   5 – 1   8 – 6   6 – 3   9 – 2   10 – 2

```
0   1   2   3   4   5   6   7   8   9   10
```

• ## Write the answers on the footprints.

Now try this!

$$7 - 2 =$$ $$9 - 4 =$$ $$10 - 3 =$$

Teachers' note Make sure the children know that when they subtract, the numbers become smaller. Check that they count the number of jumps on the number line. It is important that children do not become over-reliant on this strategy. Number lines should be seen as a stepping stone towards mental strategies such as counting back and quick recall.

Developing Numeracy Calculations Year R
© A & C Black

Misty mountains

- **Write how many mountains.**

- **Write how many mountains are behind the cloud.**

> Count how many you can see. Then count on up to 10.

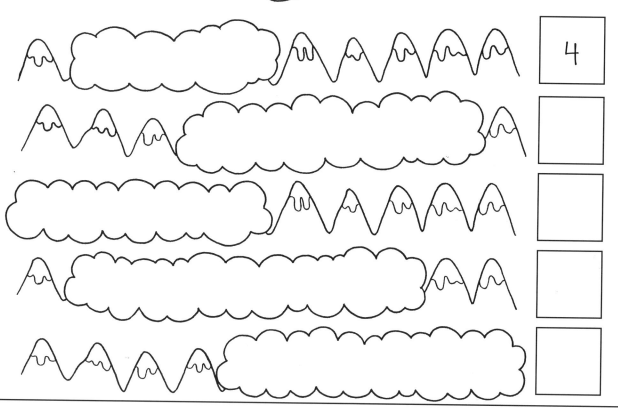

| 4 |

Now try this!

- **There are 10 goats on the hillside.**
- **Write how many are hiding.**

Teachers' note Check that the children can count on from one number to another, keeping a tally of 'how many' on their fingers.

**Developing Numeracy
Calculations Year R
© A & C Black**

Fairground game

- **Play with a partner.**
- **Roll a dice. Move your counter.**

The winner is the first to collect 10p.

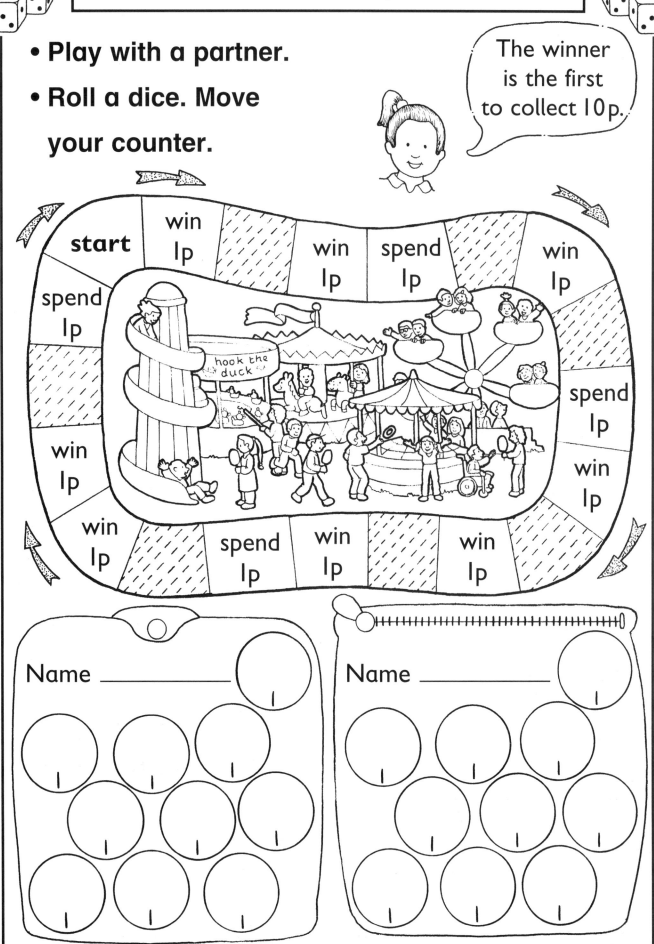

Name _____

Name _____

Teachers' note Each pair of children needs a copy of the sheet, a dice, two counters in different colours and twenty 1p coins (or cubes to represent coins). When the children win 1p, they should put a coin on one of the circles in their purse. When they spend 1p, they should take a coin out of the purse (if they can). They keep going round the track until one of the children fills their purse.

Developing Numeracy Calculations Year R
© A & C Black

In the gym

- **Draw the** total **balls.**

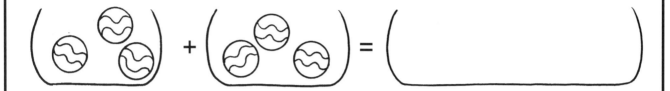

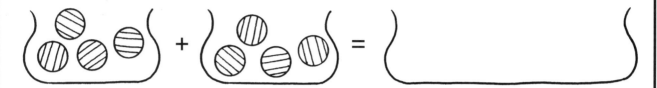

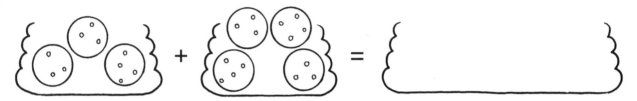

- **Draw how many beanbags are left.**

- **Draw beanbags to show your own** addition

or subtraction .

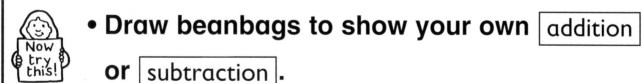

Teachers' note If necessary, revise 'total' and 'take away'. Some children may find it helpful to use counters to represent the balls and beanbags.

**Developing Numeracy
Calculations Year R
© A & C Black**

The bus stop

0 1 2 3 4 5 6 7 8 9 10

- **Write how many people there will be.**

4 more people

How many? **7**

3 more people

How many?

2 fewer people

How many?

3 fewer people

How many?

Now try this!

- **Write** **more** **or** **fewer** .
- **Write how many people.**

2 _____ people

How many?

3 _____ people

How many?

Teachers' note Introduce or revise 'more' and 'fewer'. It can be challenging for children to distinguish between when to use 'fewer' and when to use 'less'. Explain that 'fewer' is used for objects that can be counted (for example, 'fewer people'), whereas 'less' is used for quantities that cannot be counted (for example, 'less milk').

Developing Numeracy Calculations Year R © A & C Black

Hidden gold

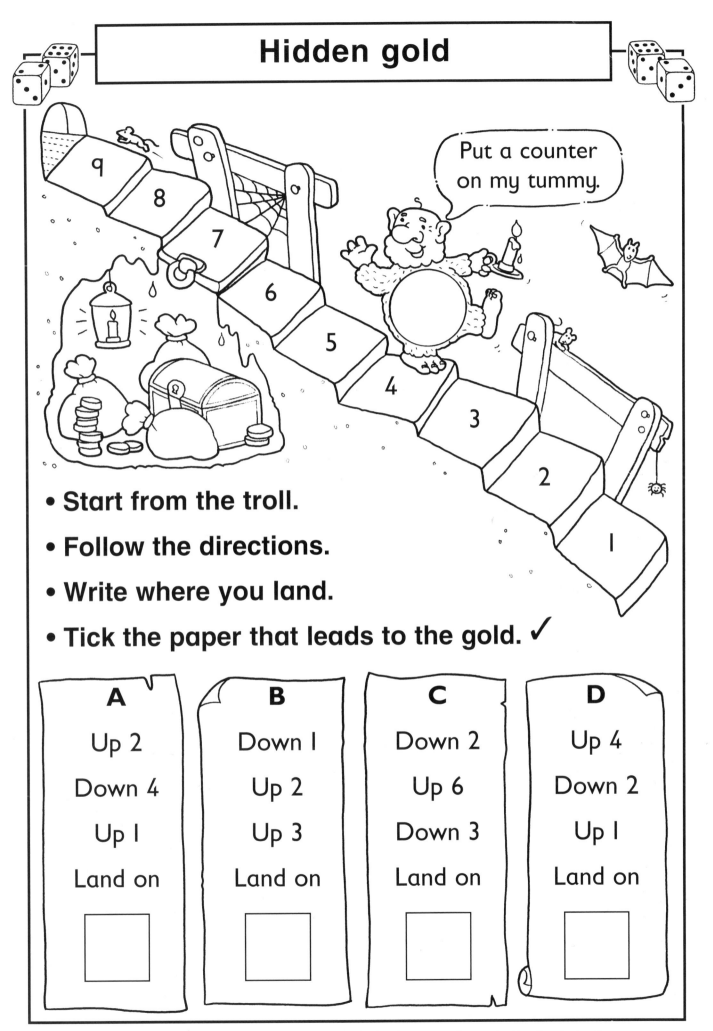

Put a counter on my tummy.

9
8
7
6
5
4
3
2
1

- **Start from the troll.**
- **Follow the directions.**
- **Write where you land.**
- **Tick the paper that leads to the gold.** ✓

A	B	C	D
Up 2	Down 1	Down 2	Up 4
Down 4	Up 2	Up 6	Down 2
Up 1	Up 3	Down 3	Up 1
Land on	Land on	Land on	Land on

Teachers' note The children could work in pairs. Ensure they realise that they must end up on step 7 in order to reach the gold. Relate the up and down movements to adding and subtracting. As an extension, the children could make up their own directions for finding the gold.

**Developing Numeracy
Calculations Year R
© A & C Black**

Batty hats

- **Join each hat to its answer.**

Use counters if you need to.

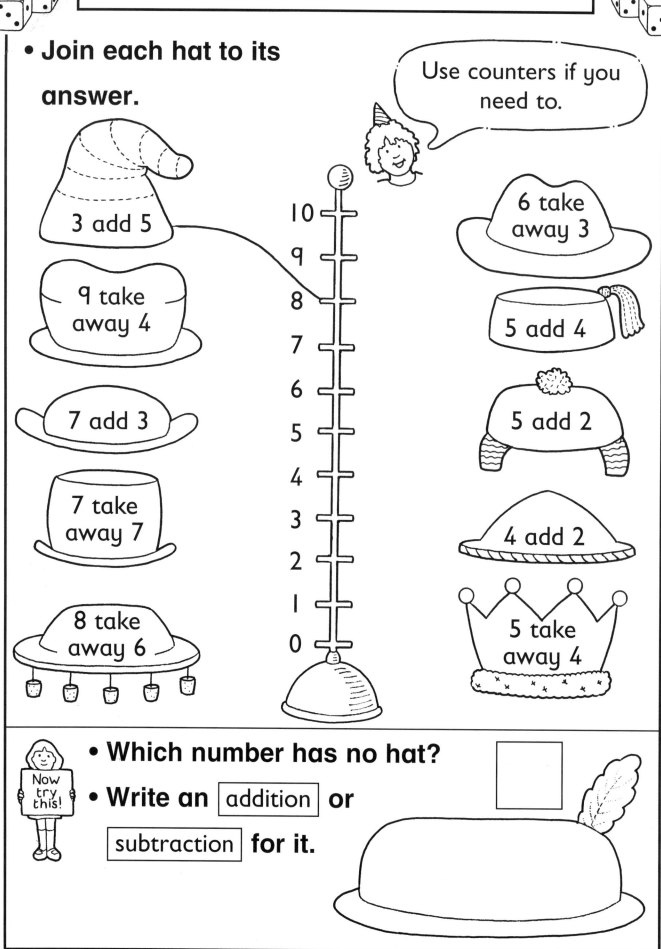

3 add 5

9 take away 4

7 add 3

7 take away 7

8 take away 6

10
9
8
7
6
5
4
3
2
1
0

6 take away 3

5 add 4

5 add 2

4 add 2

5 take away 4

- **Which number has no hat?**
- **Write an** addition **or** subtraction **for it.**

Now try this!

Teachers' note If necessary, revise 'add' and 'take away'. Some children may find it helpful to use counters as an aid. For the extension activity, explain that the calculation can be an addition or subtraction and can use a mix of numbers and words.

**Developing Numeracy
Calculations Year R
© A & C Black**

Busy beavers

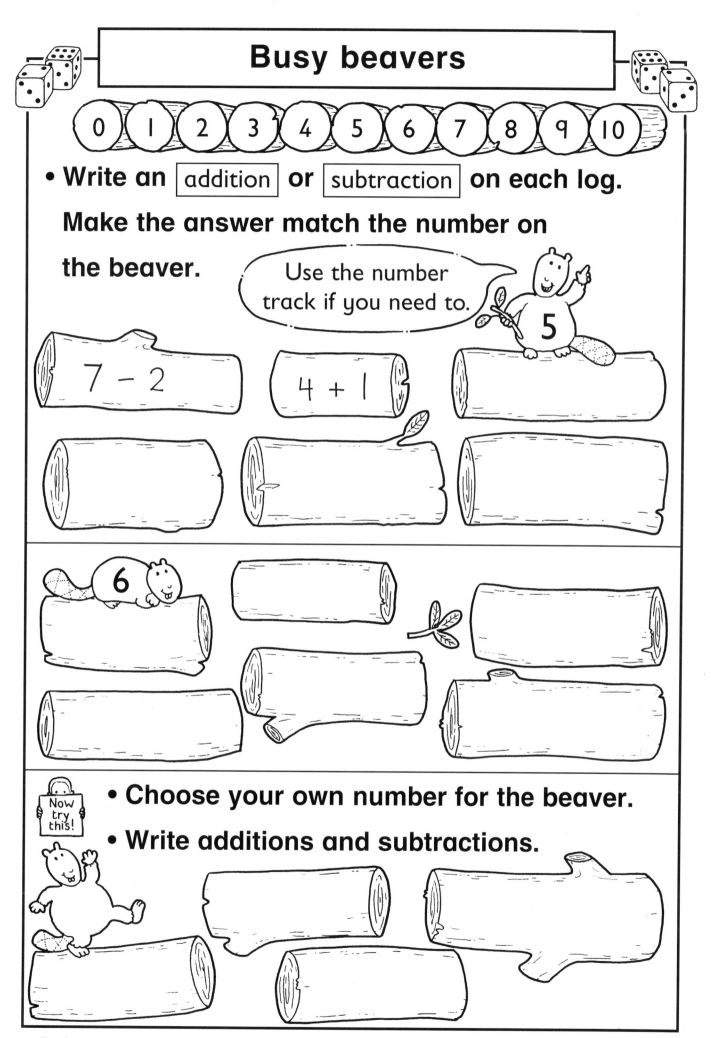

Number track: 0 1 2 3 4 5 6 7 8 9 10

- Write an [addition] or [subtraction] on each log.

Make the answer match the number on the beaver.

Use the number track if you need to.

5

7 – 2

4 + 1

6

- Choose your own number for the beaver.
- Write additions and subtractions.

Now try this!

Teachers' note Introduce the activity by playing 'What is the question?' (see page 5). Encourage the children to write a mix of additions and subtractions for each answer. With prompting, some children may be able to write calculations such as 2 + 2 + 2. Ask the children to say the calculations as number sentences, using words such as add, plus, take away and minus.

**Developing Numeracy
Calculations Year R
© A & C Black**

Secret message

- ## Look at the code.

1	2	3	4	5	6	7	8	9	10
e	h	f	a	k	s	t	i	m	l

- ## Follow each clue.

- ## Find the number.

- ## Write the matching letter.

Start at 5

Count on 3

The letter is

i

Start at 6

Count on 4

The letter is

Start at 2

Count on 6

The letter is

Start at 8

Count back 3

The letter is

Start at 7

Count back 6

The letter is

Start at 4

Count on 5

The letter is

Start at 10

Count back 6

The letter is

Start at 2

Count on 5

The letter is

Start at 9

Count back 7

The letter is

Start at 10

Count back 4

The letter is

- ## Write the message.

_____

Teachers' note Make sure the children know that when they count on, the numbers become larger, and when they count back, the numbers become smaller. Check that the children understand how to use the code grid. They can work in pairs on this activity. As an extension, they could write clues to spell 'fish' and 'tail', using the same code grid.

**Developing Numeracy
Calculations Year R
© A & C Black**

Dragon fire

| 0 | 1 | 2 | 3 | 4 | 5 | 6 | 7 | 8 | 9 | 10 |

The dragon has burned the signs!

- Write the missing signs. Use the number track to help you.

+ plus sign
– minus sign

4 (+) 5 = 9   8 ( ) 3 = 5   3 ( ) 3 = 6

10 ( ) 5 = 5   2 ( ) 6 = 8   3 ( ) 7 = 10

5 ( ) 5 = 0   0 ( ) 7 = 7   5 ( ) 4 = 1

- Write 2 more puzzles for a friend.

Now try this!

☐ ( ) ☐ = ☐

☐ ( ) ☐ = ☐

Don't write the signs!

Teachers' note Revise the plus and minus signs. The children can use counters or the number track as an aid. In the extension activity, they may find it helpful to write the entire calculation and then erase the sign. Ensure the children realise that + or – could go in problems such as 7 ☐ 0 = 7.

**Developing Numeracy
Calculations Year R
© A & C Black**

Lorry puzzles

0 1 2 3 4 5 6 7 8 9 10

- ## Write numbers in the gaps.

There are several possible answers.

7 – 1 = 6

7 – =

+ = 7

+ = 7

8 – =

8 – =

+ = 8

+ = 8

– = 0

– = 0

- ## Write 2 more puzzles for a friend.

Now try this!

– =

+ =

Teachers' note Before beginning, revise the plus and minus signs and play 'What is the question?' (see page 5). The children can work in pairs or groups, using counters or the number track. Ask them to say the calculations as number sentences, using words such as add, plus, take away and minus. In the extension, they should write complete calculations in pencil and then erase some of the numbers.

Developing Numeracy Calculations Year R © A & C Black